TABLE OF CONTENT

STOMACH

ULCER

DIET

BOOK

PEPTIC ULCER DISEASE

Peptic ulcer disease (PUD) is a break in the inner lining of the stomach, the first part of the small intestine, or sometimes the lower esophagus. An ulcer in the stomach is called a gastric ulcer, while one in the first part of the intestines is a duodenal ulcer. The most common symptoms of a duodenal ulcer are waking at night with upper abdominal pain and upper abdominal pain that improves with eating. With a gastric ulcer, the pain may worsen with eating. The pain is often described as a burning or dull ache. Other symptoms include belching, vomiting, weight loss, or poor appetite. About a third of older people have no symptoms. Complications may include bleeding, perforation, and blockage of the stomach. Bleeding occurs in as many as 15% of cases.

Common causes include the bacteria Helicobacter pylori and non-steroidal anti-inflammatory drugs (NSAIDs). Other, less common causes include tobacco smoking, stress as a result of other serious health conditions,

Behçet's disease, Zollinger–Ellison syndrome, Crohn's disease, and liver cirrhosis. Older people are more sensitive to the ulcer-causing effects of NSAIDs. The diagnosis is typically suspected due to the presenting symptoms with confirmation by either endoscopy or barium swallow. H. pylori can be diagnosed by testing the blood for antibodies, a urea breath test, testing the stool for signs of the bacteria, or a biopsy of the stomach. Other conditions that produce similar symptoms include stomach cancer, coronary heart disease, and inflammation of the stomach lining or gallbladder inflammation.

Diet does not play an important role in either causing or preventing ulcers. Treatment includes stopping smoking, stopping use of NSAIDs, stopping alcohol, and taking medications to decrease stomach acid. The medication used to decrease acid is usually either a proton pump inhibitor (PPI) or an H2 blocker, with four weeks of treatment initially recommended. Ulcers due to H. pylori are treated with a combination of medications, such as amoxicillin, clarithromycin, and a PPI. Antibiotic resistance is increasing and thus treatment may not always be effective. Bleeding ulcers may be treated by endoscopy, with open surgery typically only used in cases in which it is not successful.

Peptic ulcers are present in around 4% of the population. New ulcers were found in around 87.4 million people worldwide during 2015. About 10% of people develop a peptic ulcer at some point in their life. Peptic ulcers resulted in 267,500 deaths in 2015, down from 327,000 in 1990.

The first description of a perforated peptic ulcer was in 1670, in Princess Henrietta of England. H. pylori was first identified as causing peptic ulcers by Barry Marshall and Robin Warren in the late 20th century, a discovery for which they received the Nobel Prize in 2005.

SIGNS AND SYMPTOMS

Signs and symptoms of a peptic ulcer can include one or more of the following:

• abdominal pain, classically epigastric, strongly correlated with mealtimes. In case of duodenal ulcers, the pain appears about three hours after taking a meal and wakes the person from sleep;

• bloating and abdominal fullness;

• waterbrash (a rush of saliva after an episode of regurgitation to dilute the acid in esophagus, although this is more associated with gastroesophageal reflux disease);

• nausea and copious vomiting;

• loss of appetite and weight loss, in gastric ulcer;

• weight gain, in duodenal ulcer, as the pain is relieved by eating;

• hematemesis (vomiting of blood); this can occur due to bleeding directly from a gastric ulcer or from damage to the esophagus from severe/continuing vomiting.

- melena (tarry, foul-smelling feces due to presence of oxidized iron from hemoglobin);

- rarely, an ulcer can lead to a gastric or duodenal perforation, which leads to acute peritonitis and extreme, stabbing pain, and requires immediate surgery.

A history of heartburn or gastroesophageal reflux disease (GERD) and use of certain medications can raise the suspicion for peptic ulcer. Medicines associated with peptic ulcer include NSAIDs (non-steroid anti-inflammatory drugs) that inhibit cyclooxygenase and most glucocorticoids (e.g., dexamethasone and prednisolone).

In people over the age of 45 with more than two weeks of the above symptoms, the odds for peptic ulceration are high enough to warrant rapid investigation by esophagogastroduodenoscopy.

The timing of symptoms in relation to the meal may differentiate between gastric and duodenal ulcers. A gastric ulcer would give epigastric pain during the meal, associated with nausea and vomiting, as gastric acid production is increased as food enters the stomach. Pain in duodenal ulcers would be aggravated by hunger and relieved by a meal and is associated with night pain.

Also, the symptoms of peptic ulcers may vary with the location of the ulcer and the person's age. Furthermore, typical ulcers tend to heal and recur, and as a result the pain may occur for few days and weeks and then wane or disappear. Usually, children and the elderly do not develop any symptoms unless complications have arisen.

A burning or gnawing feeling in the stomach area lasting between 30 minutes and 3 hours commonly accompanies ulcers. This pain can be misinterpreted as hunger, indigestion, or heartburn. Pain is usually caused by the ulcer, but it may be aggravated by the stomach acid when it comes into contact with the ulcerated area. The pain caused by peptic ulcers can be felt anywhere from the navel up to the sternum, it may last from few minutes to several hours, and it may be worse when the stomach is empty. Also, sometimes the pain may flare at night, and it can commonly be temporarily relieved by eating foods that buffer stomach acid or by taking anti-acid medication. However, peptic ulcer disease symptoms may be different for every sufferer.

Complications

• Gastrointestinal bleeding is the most common complication. Sudden large bleeding can be life-threatening. It is associated with 5% to 10% death rate.

- Perforation (a hole in the wall of the gastrointestinal tract) following a gastric ulcer often leads to catastrophic consequences if left untreated. Erosion of the gastrointestinal wall by the ulcer leads to spillage of the stomach or intestinal contents into the abdominal cavity, leading to an acute chemical peritonitis. The first sign is often sudden intense abdominal pain, as seen in Valentino's syndrome. Posterior gastric wall perforation may lead to bleeding due to the involvement of gastroduodenal artery that lies posterior to the first part of the duodenum. The death rate in this case is 20%.

• Penetration is a form of perforation in which the hole leads to and the ulcer continues into adjacent organs such as the liver and pancreas.

• Gastric outlet obstruction (stenosis) is a narrowing of the pyloric canal by scarring and swelling of the gastric antrum and duodenum due to peptic ulcers. The person often presents with severe vomiting.

- Cancer is included in the differential diagnosis (elucidated by biopsy), Helicobacter pylori as the etiological factor making it 3 to 6 times more likely to develop stomach cancer from the ulcer. The risk for developing gastrointestinal cancer also appears to be slightly higher with gastric ulcers

CAUSE OF STOMACH ULCER

H. pylori

Helicobacter pylori is one of the major causative factors of peptic ulcer disease. It secretes urease to create an alkaline environment, which is suitable for its survival. It expresses blood group antigen adhesin (BabA) and outer inflammatory protein adhesin (OipA), which enables it to attach to the gastric epithelium. The bacterium also expresses virulence factors such as CagA and PicB, which cause stomach mucosal inflammation.

The VacA gene encodes for vacuolating cytotoxin, but its mechanism of causing peptic ulcers is unclear. Such stomach mucosal inflammation can be associated with hyperchlorhydria (increased stomach acid secretion) or hypochlorhydria (reduced stomach acid secretion). Inflammatory cytokines inhibit the parietal cell acid secretion. H. pylori also secretes certain products that inhibit hydrogen potassium ATPase; activate calcitonin gene-related peptide sensory neurons, which increases somatostatin secretion to inhibit acid production by parietal cells; and inhibit gastrin secretion. This reduction in acid production causes gastric ulcers. On the other hand, increased acid production at the pyloric antrum is associated with duodenal ulcers in 10% to 15% of H. pylori infection cases. In this case, somatostatin production is reduced and gastrin production is increased, leading to increased histamine secretion from the enterochromaffin cells, thus increasing acid production. An acidic environment at the antrum causes metaplasia of the duodenal cells, causing duodenal ulcers.

Human immune response toward the bacteria also determines the emergence of peptic ulcer disease. The human IL1B gene encodes for Interleukin 1 beta, and other genes that encode for tumour necrosis factor (TNF) and Lymphotoxin alpha also play a role in gastric inflammation.

NSAIDs

Taking nonsteroidal anti-inflammatory drugs (NSAIDs) such as aspirin can increase the risk of peptic ulcer disease by four times compared to non-users. The risk of getting a peptic ulcer is two times for aspirin users. Risk of bleeding increases if NSAIDs are combined with selective serotonin reuptake inhibitor (SSRI), corticosteroids, antimineralocorticoids, and anticoagulants. The gastric mucosa protects itself from gastric acid with a layer of mucus, the secretion of which is stimulated by certain prostaglandins. NSAIDs block the function of cyclooxygenase 1 (COX-1), which is essential for the production of these prostaglandins. Besides this, NSAIDs also inhibit stomach mucosa cells proliferation and mucosal blood flow, reducing bicarbonate and mucus secretion, which reduces the integrity of the mucosa. Another type of NSAIDs, called COX-2 selective anti-inflammatory drugs (such as celecoxib), preferentially inhibit COX-2, which is less essential in the gastric mucosa. This reduces the probability of getting peptic ulcers; however, it can still delay ulcer healing for those who already have a peptic ulcer.

Peptic ulcers caused by NSAIDs differ from those caused by H. pylori as the latter's appear as a consequence of inflammation of the mucosa (presence of neutrophil and submucosal edema), the former instead as a consequence of a direct damage of the NSAID molecule against COX enzymes, altering the hydrophobic state of the mucus, the permeability of the lining epithelium and mitochondrial machinery of the cell itself. In this way NSAID's ulcers tend to complicate faster and dig deeper in the tissue causing more complications, often asymptomatically till a great portion of the tissue is involved.

Stress

Stress due to serious health problems, such as those requiring treatment in an intensive care unit, is well described as a cause of peptic ulcers, which are also known as stress ulcers.

While chronic life stress was once believed to be the main cause of ulcers, this is no longer the case. It is, however, still occasionally believed to play a role. This may be due to the well-documented effects of stress on gastric physiology, increasing the risk in those with other causes, such as H. pylori or NSAID use.

Diet

Dietary factors, such as spice consumption, were hypothesized to cause ulcers until the late 20th century, but have been shown to be of relatively minor importance. Caffeine and coffee, also commonly thought to cause or exacerbate ulcers, appear to have little effect. Similarly, while studies have found that alcohol consumption increases risk when associated with H. pylori infection, it does not seem to independently increase risk. Even when coupled with H. pylori infection, the increase is modest in comparison to the primary risk factor.

Other

Other causes of peptic ulcer disease include gastric ischaemia, drugs, metabolic disturbances, cytomegalovirus (CMV), upper abdominal radiotherapy, Crohn's disease, and vasculitis. Gastrinomas

(Zollinger–Ellison syndrome), or rare gastrin-secreting tumors, also cause multiple and difficult-to-heal ulcers.

It is still unclear if smoking increases the risk of getting peptic ulcers.

DIAGNOSIS OF STOMACH ULCER

The diagnosis is mainly established based on the characteristic symptoms. Stomach pain is usually the first signal of a peptic ulcer. In some cases, doctors may treat ulcers without diagnosing them with specific tests and observe whether the symptoms resolve, thus indicating that their primary diagnosis was accurate.

More specifically, peptic ulcers erode the muscularis mucosae, at minimum reaching to the level of the submucosa (contrast with erosions, which do not involve the muscularis mucosae).

Confirmation of the diagnosis is made with the help of tests such as endoscopies or barium contrast x-rays. The tests are typically ordered if the symptoms do not resolve after a few weeks of treatment, or when they first appear in a person who is over age 45 or who has other symptoms such as weight loss, because stomach cancer can cause similar symptoms. Also, when severe ulcers resist treatment, particularly if a person has several ulcers or the ulcers are in unusual places, a doctor may suspect an underlying condition that causes the stomach to overproduce acid.

An esophagogastroduodenoscopy (EGD), a form of endoscopy, also known as a gastroscopy, is carried out on people in whom a peptic ulcer is suspected. It is also the gold standard of diagnosis for peptic ulcer disease. By direct visual identification, the location and severity of an ulcer can be described. Moreover, if no ulcer is present, EGD can often provide an alternative diagnosis.

One of the reasons that blood tests are not reliable for accurate peptic ulcer diagnosis on their own is their inability to differentiate between past exposure to the bacteria and current infection. Additionally, a false negative result is possible with a blood test if the person has recently been taking certain drugs, such as antibiotics or proton-pump inhibitors.

The diagnosis of Helicobacter pylori can be made by:

• Urea breath test (noninvasive and does not require EGD);

- Direct culture from an EGD biopsy specimen; this is difficult and can be expensive. Most labs are not set up to perform H. pylori cultures;

- Direct detection of urease activity in a biopsy specimen by rapid urease test;

- Measurement of antibody levels in the blood (does not require EGD). It is still somewhat controversial whether a positive antibody without EGD is enough to warrant eradication therapy;

- Stool antigen test;

- Histological examination and staining of an EGD biopsy.

The breath test uses radioactive carbon to detect H. pylori. To perform this exam, the person is asked to drink a tasteless liquid that contains the carbon as part of the substance that the bacteria breaks down. After an hour, the person is asked to blow into a sealed bag. If the person is infected with H. pylori, the breath sample will contain radioactive carbon dioxide. This test provides the advantage of being able to monitor the response to treatment used to kill the bacteria.

The possibility of other causes of ulcers, notably malignancy (gastric cancer), needs to be kept in mind. This is especially true in ulcers of the greater (large) curvature of the stomach; most are also a consequence of chronic H. pylori infection.

If a peptic ulcer perforates, air will leak from inside the gastrointestinal tract (which always contains some air) to the peritoneal cavity (which normally never contains air). This leads to "free gas" within the peritoneal cavity. If the person stands, as when having a chest X-ray, the gas will float to a position underneath the diaphragm. Therefore, gas in the peritoneal cavity, shown on an erect chest X-ray or supine lateral abdominal X-ray, is an omen of perforated peptic ulcer disease.

CLASSIFICATION

Peptic ulcers are a form of acid–peptic disorder. Peptic ulcers can be classified according to their location and other factors.

By location

- Duodenum (called duodenal ulcer)

- Esophagus (called esophageal ulcer)

- Stomach (called gastric ulcer)

- Meckel's diverticulum (called Meckel's diverticulum ulcer; is very tender with palpation)

Modified Johnson

• Type I: Ulcer along the body of the stomach, most often along the lesser curve at incisura angularis along the locus minoris resistantiae. Not associated with acid hypersecretion.

• Type II: Ulcer in the body in combination with duodenal ulcers. Associated with acid oversecretion.

• Type III: In the pyloric channel within 3 cm of pylorus. Associated with acid oversecretion.

• Type IV: Proximal gastroesophageal ulcer.

- Type V: Can occur throughout the stomach. Associated with the chronic use of NSAIDs (such as ibuprofen).

Macroscopic appearance

Gastric ulcers are most often localized on the lesser curvature of the stomach. The ulcer is a round to oval parietal defect ("hole"), 2–4 cm diameter, with a smooth base and perpendicular borders. These borders are not elevated or irregular in the acute form of peptic ulcer, and regular but with elevated borders and inflammatory surrounding in the chronic form. In the ulcerative form of gastric cancer, the borders are irregular. Surrounding mucosa may present radial folds, as a consequence of the parietal scarring.

Microscopic appearance

A gastric peptic ulcer is a mucosal perforation that penetrates the muscularis mucosae and lamina propria, usually produced by acid-pepsin aggression. Ulcer margins are perpendicular and present chronic gastritis. During the active phase, the base of the ulcer shows 4 zones:

fibrinoid necrosis, inflammatory exudate, granulation tissue and fibrous tissue. The fibrous base of the ulcer may contain vessels with thickened wall or with thrombosis.

Differential diagnosis

Conditions that may appear similar include:

- Gastritis

- Stomach cancer

- Gastroesophageal reflux disease

- Pancreatitis

- Hepatic congestion

- Cholecystitis

- Biliary colic

- Inferior myocardial infarction

- Referred pain (pleurisy, pericarditis)

- Superior mesenteric artery syndrome

.

PREVENTION OF STOMACH ULCER

Prevention of peptic ulcer disease for those who are taking NSAIDs (with low cardiovascular risk) can be achieved by adding a proton pump inhibitor (PPI), an H2 antagonist, or misoprostol. NSAIDs of the COX-2 inhibitors type may reduce the rate of ulcers when compared to non-selective NSAIDs. PPI is the most popular agent in peptic ulcer prevention. However, there is no evidence that H2 antagonists can prevent stomach bleeding for those taking NSAIDs. Although misoprostol is effective in preventing peptic ulcer, its properties of promoting abortion and causing gastrointestinal distress limit its use. For those with high cardiovascular risk, naproxen with PPI can be a useful choice. Otherwise, low-dose aspirin, celecoxib, and PPI can also be used.

Management

Eradication therapy

Once the diagnosis of H. pylori is confirmed, the first-line treatment would be a triple regimen in which pantoprazole and clarithromycin are combined with either amoxicillin or metronidazole. This treatment regimen can be given for 7–14 days. However, its effectiveness in eradicating H. pylori has been reducing from 90% to 70%. However, the rate of eradication can be increased by doubling the dosage of pantoprazole or increasing the duration of treatment to 14 days. Quadruple therapy (pantoprazole, clarithromycin, amoxicillin, and metronidazole) can also be used. The quadruple therapy can achieve an eradication rate of 90%. If the clarithromycin resistance rate is higher than 15% in an area, the usage of clarithromycin should be abandoned. Instead, bismuth-containing quadruple therapy can be used (pantoprazole, bismuth citrate, tetracycline, and metronidazole) for 14 days. The bismuth therapy can also achieve an eradication rate of 90% and can be used as second-line therapy when the first-line triple-regimen therapy has failed

NSAIDs induced ulcers

NSAID-associated ulcers heal in 6 to 8 weeks provided the NSAIDs are withdrawn with the introduction of proton pump inhibitors (PPI).

Bleeding

For those with bleeding peptic ulcers, fluid replacement with crystalloids is sometimes given to maintain volume in the blood vessels. Maintaining haemoglobin at greater than 7 g/dL (70 g/L) through restrictive blood transfusion has been associated with reduced rate of death. Glasgow-Blatchford score is used to determine whether a person should be treated inside a hospital or as an outpatient. Intravenous PPIs can suppress stomach bleeding more quickly than oral ones. A neutral stomach pH is required to keep platelets in place and prevent clot lysis. Tranexamic acid and antifibrinolytic agents are not useful in treating peptic ulcer disease.

Early endoscopic therapy can help to stop bleeding by using cautery, endoclip, or epinephrine injection. Treatment is indicated if there is active bleeding in the stomach, visible vessels, or an adherent clot.

Endoscopy is also helpful in identifying people who are suitable for hospital discharge. Prokinetic agents such as erythromycin and metoclopramide can be given before endoscopy to improve endoscopic view. Either high- or low-dose PPIs are equally effective in reducing bleeding after endoscopy. High-dose intravenous PPI is defined as a bolus dose of 80 mg followed by an infusion of 8 mg per hour for 72 hours in other words, the continuous infusion of PPI of greater than 192 mg per day. Intravenous PPI can be changed to oral once there is no high risk of rebleeding from peptic ulcer.

For those with hypovolemic shock and ulcer size of greater than 2 cm, there is a high chance that the endoscopic treatment would fail. Therefore, surgery and angiographic embolism are reserved for these complicated cases. However, there is a higher rate of complication for those who underwent surgery to patch the stomach bleeding site when compared to repeated endoscopy. Angiographic embolisation has a higher rebleeding rate but a similar rate of death to surgery.

Anticoagulants

According to expert opinion, for those who are already on anticoagulants, the international normalized ratio (INR) should be kept at 1.5. For aspirin users who required endoscopic treatment for bleeding peptic ulcer, there is two times increased risk of rebleeding but with 10 times reduced risk of death at 8 weeks following the resumption of aspirin. For those who were on double antiplatelet agents for indwelling stent in blood vessels, both antiplatelet agents should not be stopped because there is a high risk of stent thrombosis. For those who were under warfarin treatment, fresh frozen plasma (FFP), vitamin K, prothrombin complex concentrates, or recombinant factor VIIa can be given to reverse the effect of warfarin. High doses of vitamin K should be avoided to reduce the time for rewarfarinisation once the stomach bleeding has stopped. Prothrombin complex concentrates are preferred for severe bleeding. Recombinant factor VIIa is reserved for life-threatening bleeding because of its high risk of thromboembolism. Direct oral anticoagulants (DOAC) are recommended instead of warfarin as they are more effective in preventing thromboembolism. In case of bleeding caused by DOAC, activated charcoal within 4 hours is the antidote of choice.

STOMACH ULCER DIET RECIPES

Here are some ulcer recipes you can try out , these recipes are explained by listing the ingredients alongside the instructions on how to go about it;

Simple Delicious Salad

Ingredients

- ¼ pound bacon

- 2 eggs

- ½ head lettuce

- 1 carrot, shredded

- 1 tomato, sliced

- 1 tablespoon corn oil

- 1 tablespoon red wine vinegar

- salt and pepper to taste

Directions

- Step 1

Place bacon in a large, deep skillet. Cook over medium high heat until evenly brown. Drain, crumble and set aside.

- Step 2

Place eggs in a saucepan and cover with cold water. Bring water to a boil and immediately remove from heat.

Cover and let eggs stand in hot water for 10 to 12 minutes. Remove from hot water, cool, peel and chop.

- Step 3

Place lettuce in a salad bowl along with the carrot and tomato. Sprinkle with bacon and eggs and toss.

- Step 4

Drizzle oil over salad. Add vinegar and salt and pepper to taste.

Marry-Me Chicken

Ingredients

- 1 ½ pounds skinless, boneless chicken breast halves

- 2 tablespoons butter

- 3 cloves garlic, minced

- ½ teaspoon dried oregano

- ¼ teaspoon ground thyme

- ½ cup chicken broth, divided

- ½ pound bacon

- 1 (16 ounce) package angel hair pasta

- 1 tablespoon all-purpose flour

- ½ cup freshly shaved Parmesan cheese

- ¼ cup whipping cream

- ¼ cup chopped sun-dried tomatoes

- 1 pinch red pepper flakes

- salt to taste

Directions

- Step 1

Preheat the oven to 350 degrees F (175 degrees C).

- Step 2

Place chicken breasts on a flat work surface. Slice horizontally through the middle, being careful not to cut all the way through to the other side. Open the 2 sides and spread them out like an open book to butterfly.

- Step 3

Melt butter in a large, oven-safe skillet over medium-high heat. Add garlic, oregano, thyme. Saute until fragrant, about 30 seconds. Add chicken and cook until golden brown but not fully cooked, 3 to 4 minutes per side. Pour 1/4 cup chicken broth into the skillet.

- Step 4

Bake in the preheated oven until chicken is no longer pink in the centers and juices run clear, about 15 minutes.

- Step 5

Meanwhile, place bacon in a large skillet and cook over medium-high heat, turning occasionally, until evenly browned, about 10 minutes. Drain bacon slices on paper towels and let cool enough to handle, about 5 minutes; chop.

- Step 6

At the same time, bring a large pot of lightly salted water to a boil. Cook angel hair pasta in the boiling water, stirring occasionally, until tender yet firm to the bite, 4 to 5 minutes. Drain and keep warm.

- Step 7

Remove skillet from the oven and transfer chicken to a plate, reserving juices in the skillet. Keep chicken warm and place skillet on the stovetop.

- Step 8

Whisk flour into the skillet over medium heat. Add remaining chicken broth, Parmesan cheese, and whipping cream. Whisk until combined. Add sun-dried tomatoes, red pepper flakes, and salt. Add bacon and chicken back into the skillet. Serve on top of hot cooked pasta.

Chocolate-Cranberry Energy Bars

Ingredients

- ½ cup raw almonds

- ½ cup walnuts

- ½ cup pitted dates

- ½ cup dried cranberries

- ⅛ cup shredded coconut

- 3 teaspoons unsweetened cocoa powder

- 1 teaspoon vanilla extract

Directions

- Step 1

Preheat the oven to 350 degrees F (175 degrees C). Line a baking sheet with parchment paper.

- Step 2

Pulse almonds and walnuts together in the bowl of a food processor until chopped. Add dates and cranberries, a little at a time, and continue to chop. Add coconut, cocoa, and vanilla extract. Process to desired consistency.

- Step 3

Roll dough into a 2-inch wide log and cut into ten 3/4-inch thick pucks. Place on the prepared baking sheet.

- Step 4

Bake in the preheated oven until set, about 10 minutes.

Joe's Perfect 'Anti-Sour Mix' Margarita

Ingredients

- kosher salt

- 1 cup ice cubes

- 2 fluid ounces silver tequila

- 1 fluid ounce orange liqueur

- 1 fluid ounce sweetened lime juice (such as Rose's®)

- 2 ounces grapefruit flavored soda

Directions

- Step 1

Pour 1/4 to 1/2 inch of salt onto a small, shallow plate. Moisten the rim of a large glass with water and dip into the salt. Fill the glass with ice, and set aside.

- Step 2

Pour the tequila, orange liqueur, and lime juice into a cocktail shaker over ice. Cover, and shake until the outside of the shaker has frosted. Strain into the prepared glass. Slowly pour in grapefruit soda to serve.

Hog Maw

Ingredients

- 4 baking potatoes, peeled and cubed

- 1 large pork stomach

- 1 ½ pounds bulk pork sausage

- 1 medium head cabbage, separated into leaves and rinsed

- salt and pepper to taste

Directions

- Step 1

Preheat the oven to 375 degrees F (190 degrees C). Place the potatoes into a large pan with enough lightly salted water to cover them. Bring to a boil, and cook until tender, about 10 minutes. Drain and let cool.

- Step 2

Wash the pork stomach thoroughly in cold water. Alternate stuffing the pork stomach with potatoes, sausage, and cabbage, seasoning with a little salt and pepper, until the stomach is full. Try to make even layers, imagining how it will look when it is done and you slice it. Fold closed, and place in a shallow roasting pan. If you have any leftover stuffing ingredients, just place them in the pan around the outside.

- Step 3

Roast uncovered for 40 to 50 minutes in the preheated oven, until the sausage is cooked through and the stomach is browned and crispy. When done, slice into 2 inch slices and serve piping hot. You can make gravy out of the drippings if desired, but it is good by itself as a whole meal.

Currant Scones

Ingredients

- ¾ cup dried currants

- 4 ¾ cups all-purpose flour

- 1 tablespoon baking powder

- ¾ teaspoon baking soda

- ½ cup white sugar

- 1 ¼ teaspoons salt

- 1 cup chilled unsalted butter, cut into 1/2-inch cubes

- 1 tablespoon chilled unsalted butter, cut into 1/2-inch cubes

- 1 ½ cups buttermilk

- 1 teaspoon lemon zest

- 2 tablespoons melted butter

- ¼ cup coarse sugar crystals

Directions

- Step 1

Preheat oven to 400 degrees F (200 degrees C). Line a baking sheet with parchment paper.

- Step 2

Cover currants with warm water in a bowl and set aside to moisten.

- Step 3

Sift flour, baking powder, and baking soda in the bowl of a stand mixer. Using the paddle attachment at low speed, mix white sugar and salt into the flour mixture. Add all the unsalted butter to the mixer bowl and mix on low speed until butter cubes reduce to the size of small peas, about 30 seconds.

- Step 4

Drain currants and discard soaking water; mix currants, buttermilk, and lemon zest into the flour mixture on low speed just until the dough starts to hold together.

- Step 5

Turn dough out onto a lightly floured work surface and gently shape into a rectangle 18 inches long, 5 inches wide, and 1 1/2 inches thick. Brush dough with melted butter and sprinkle with sugar crystals.

- Step 6

Cut the dough in half crosswise with a sharp knife; cut each half into thirds, and cut each third diagonally to make 12 triangular-shaped scones. Place on the prepared baking sheet.

- Step 7

Bake in the preheated oven until scones are lightly golden brown, about 18 minutes. Eat warm.

Butter Popcorn With Sumac

Ingredients

- ¼ cup butter

- 2 ½ tablespoons vegetable oil, divided

- 1 teaspoon sumac powder

- 1 teaspoon chili powder

- ¼ teaspoon salt

- ¾ cup unpopped popcorn

Directions

- Step 1

Combine butter and 1/2 tablespoon oil in a saucepan over medium-low heat; cook and stir until butter is just melted, 1 to 2 minutes. Stir sumac, chili powder, and salt into butter-oil mixture.

- Step 2

Heat 2 tablespoons oil in a large saucepan over high heat. Add 3 popcorn kernels to the oil and cover saucepan with a lid. Once the 3 kernels have popped, the oil is ready. Add the remaining popcorn, cover saucepan, and cook popcorn, shaking saucepan constantly, until you no longer hear popping. Remove saucepan from heat.

- Step 3

Transfer popcorn to a large heat-proof bowl and let sit for 2 minutes to ensure better coverage by the butter.

- Step 4

Pour half of the butter mixture in a second large bowl and swirl it around the bottom and sides; add popcorn and mix with a big spoon. Transfer the popcorn back in the first large bowl; stir again. Pour remaining half butter mixture into the second bowl and swirl around again; add the popcorn in and mix again.

Honey-Quinoa Salad with Cherries and Cashews

Ingredients

- 1 cup water

- ⅔ cup quinoa, rinsed and drained

- ½ teaspoon salt, divided

- ¼ cup honey

- 2 tablespoons grated fresh ginger

- 2 tablespoons white wine vinegar

- 2 tablespoons lime juice

- 1 clove garlic, minced

- ¼ teaspoon ground black pepper

- ¼ cup olive oil

- 1 cup fresh dark sweet cherries, pitted and halved

- ½ cup coarsely chopped cashews

- ½ cup dried apricots, thinly sliced

- ¼ cup thinly sliced red onion

- 4 cups torn Bibb lettuce

Directions

- Step 1

Stir water, quinoa, and 1/4 teaspoon salt together in a saucepan; bring to a boil. Reduce heat; simmer, covered, until liquid is absorbed, about 10 minutes. Remove from heat. Let stand for 10 minutes.

- Step 2

Meanwhile, whisk honey, ginger, vinegar, lime juice, garlic, remaining 1/4 teaspoon salt, and pepper together in a small bowl. Slowly add olive oil, whisking constantly, until fully incorporated.

- Step 3

Fluff quinoa with a fork. Stir together quinoa, cherries, cashews, dried apricots, and red onion in a large bowl. Add lettuce. Drizzle with 1/2 cup honey vinaigrette; toss to coat. Serve salad with remaining vinaigrette.

Slow Cooker Bone Broth

Ingredients

- 3 pounds beef bones, or more to taste

- 3 carrots, chopped

- 2 stalks celery, chopped

- 1 onion, chopped

- 5 cloves garlic, smashed

- 1 teaspoon whole black peppercorns

- 2 bay leaves

- cold water to cover

- 2 tablespoons apple cider vinegar

- kosher salt to taste

Directions

- Step 1

Preheat oven to 375 degrees F (190 degrees C). Line a baking sheet with aluminum foil; spread beef bones out on prepared baking sheet.

- Step 2

Roast bones in the preheated oven until browned, 25 to 30 minutes.

- Step 3

Place carrots, celery, onion, garlic, peppercorns, and bay leaves in a slow cooker. Place roasted bones over vegetables; pour in enough cold water to cover bones. Add apple cider vinegar and kosher salt.

- Step 4

Cook on Low for 8 hours. Pour broth through a fine-mesh strainer into a bowl and discard any strained solids.

Savory Cinnamon Rolls

Ingredients

- 2 (.25 ounce) packages active dry yeast

- 2 ½ cups warm water (110 degrees F/45 degrees C)

- 1 (9 ounce) package yellow cake mix

- 1 teaspoon salt

- 1 teaspoon vanilla extract

- 5 cups all-purpose flour

- ½ cup butter, softened

- ¾ cup white sugar

- 2 teaspoons ground cinnamon

- 3 cups confectioners' sugar

- ⅓ cup butter, softened

- 1 ½ teaspoons vanilla extract

- 1 ½ tablespoons milk

Directions

- Step 1

In a large bowl, dissolve yeast in warm water. Let stand until creamy, about 10 minutes.

- Step 2

In a large bowl, combine the yeast mixture with the cake mix, salt and vanilla; stir well to combine. Stir in the flour; beat well. Cover bowl and let rise in a warm place for 1 hour.

- Step 3

Deflate dough and turn it out onto a well floured surface. Roll dough out into a rectangle and spread with butter. Sprinkle with cinnamon and sugar. Roll up dough and cut into 3/4 inch thick rolls. Place rolls in two lightly greased 9x13 inch baking pans. Cover and let rise until doubled, about 45 minutes.

- Step 4

Preheat oven to 350 degrees F (175 degrees C).

- Step 5

Bake rolls in preheated oven for 15 to 20 minutes. While rolls are baking, prepare the frosting. In a medium bowl, stir together confectioners' sugar, 1/3 cup butter, vanilla and milk. Let rolls cool slightly then spread with frosting.

Vegetarian Kale Soup

Ingredients

- 2 tablespoons olive oil

- 1 yellow onion, chopped

- 2 tablespoons chopped garlic

- 1 bunch kale, stems removed and leaves chopped

- 8 cups water

- 6 cubes vegetable bouillon (such as Knorr)

- 1 (15 ounce) can diced tomatoes

- 6 white potatoes, peeled and cubed

- 2 (15 ounce) cans cannellini beans (drained if desired)

- 1 tablespoon Italian seasoning

- 2 tablespoons dried parsley

- salt and pepper to taste

Directions

- Step 1

Heat the olive oil in a large soup pot; cook the onion and garlic until soft.

Stir in the kale and cook until wilted, about 2 minutes. Stir in the water, vegetable bouillon, tomatoes, potatoes, beans, Italian seasoning, and parsley. Simmer soup on medium heat for 25 minutes, or until potatoes are cooked through. Season with salt and pepper to taste.

Cacio e Pepe Lasagna

Ingredients

- olive oil, divided

- 12 lasagna noodles, broken into 2-inch pieces

- 1 (16 ounce) container fresh ricotta cheese

- ½ cup shredded mozzarella cheese

- ½ cup grated Pecorino Romano cheese

- 2 teaspoons freshly ground black pepper, divided

- 2 tablespoons grated Pecorino Romano cheese

- 2 tablespoons chopped fresh flat-leaf parsley, or to taste

- 1 pinch paprika for garnish (Optional)

Directions

- Step 1

Preheat the oven to 450 degrees F (230 degrees C). Grease four 8-ounce ramekins with 1 tablespoon olive oil.

- Step 2

Bring a large pot of lightly salted water to a boil. Cook lasagna noodles in the boiling water, stirring occasionally until tender yet firm to the bite, about 8 minutes. Drain.

- Step 3

Mix together drained noodles, ricotta cheese, mozzarella cheese, 1/2 cup Pecorino Romano cheese, and 1 1/2 teaspoons pepper in a bowl. Divide mixture among the ramekins. Top with 2 tablespoons Pecorino Romano cheese, drizzle with 1 tablespoon olive oil, and sprinkle with remaining 1/2 teaspoon black pepper.

- Step 4

Bake in the preheated oven until cheese is golden brown in spots and lasagna is heated through, about 10 minutes. Garnish with parsley and paprika, if desired.

Tortellini Alfredo with Grilled Chicken Breasts

Ingredients

Chicken:

- 2 large skinless, boneless chicken breasts

- olive oil

- 1 pinch Italian seasoning, or to taste

- 1 pinch garlic powder, or to taste

- kosher salt and freshly ground black pepper to taste

Alfredo Sauce:

- 1 (12 ounce) package frozen cheese tortellini

- ¼ cup butter

- 3 cloves garlic, minced

- 1 cup heavy cream

- 1 ¼ cups freshly grated Parmesan cheese

- 2 pinches Italian seasoning, or to taste

- freshly ground black pepper to taste

Directions

- Step 1

Preheat an outdoor grill for medium-high heat and lightly oil the grate.

- Step 2

Place chicken in a bowl and add oil, Italian seasoning, garlic powder, kosher salt, and pepper. Toss to coat.

- Step 3

Cook chicken on the preheated grill until no longer pink in the centers and the juices run clear, about 6 minutes per side. An instant-read thermometer inserted into the center should read at least 165 degrees F (74 degrees C). Remove from the grill and allow to cool.

- Step 4

Meanwhile, fill a large pot with lightly salted water and bring to a rolling boil; stir in tortellini and return to a boil. Cook uncovered, stirring occasionally, until the tortellini float to the top and the filling is hot, about 3 minutes. Drain and set aside; keep warm.

- Step 5

Slice chicken breast into bite-size pieces.

- Step 6

Melt butter in a saucepan over medium heat. Add garlic and cook, 2 to 3 minutes. Add cream and heat to room temperature, about 3 minutes more. Stir in Parmesan cheese and allow to melt, 2 to 3 minutes. Add Italian seasoning and pepper. Bring to a slow boil for about 1 minute before tossing in cooked tortellini and grilled chicken breast.

Stir-Fried Chicken With Pineapple and Peppers

Ingredients

- ¼ cup reduced-salt soy sauce

- 2 tablespoons white wine vinegar

- 2 tablespoons mirin (sweetened Asian wine)

- 1 teaspoon grated ginger root

- 2 crushed garlic cloves

- 1 tablespoon cornstarch

- 2 tablespoons oil, preferably sesame oil

- 1 pound boneless, skinless chicken breast, cut in 1-inch pieces

- 6 large green onions, cut in 1-inch pieces

- 2 cups fresh or frozen pepper strips

- 1 (20 ounce) can chunk pineapple in juice

- ¼ cup sliced almonds (Optional)

Directions

- Step 1

Combine first six ingredients; stir well.

- Step 2

Heat oil in a large skillet and stir-fry chicken until brown and done, about 5 minutes. Remove. Add green onions, peppers and pineapple to the skillet; heat through. Pour in sauce and stir until thickened. Return chicken to skillet; heat through. Serve with brown rice; top with optional almonds.

Oat and Chocolate Chip Bar Cookies

Ingredients

- 3 cups all-purpose flour

- 1 teaspoon baking soda

- ½ teaspoon salt

- 1 cup softened butter

- ¾ cup white sugar

- ¾ cup brown sugar

- ¼ cup milk

- 2 eggs

- 2 teaspoons vanilla extract

- 2 cups semisweet chocolate chips

- 2 cups rolled oats

Directions

- Step 1

Preheat oven to 350 degrees F (175 degrees C). Grease a baking pan.

- Step 2

Mix flour, baking soda, and salt together in a small bowl.

- Step 3

Cream butter, white sugar, and brown sugar together in a large bowl with an electric mixer. Add milk, eggs, and vanilla extract. Stir in flour mixture; fold in chocolate chips and oats. Spread into the prepared baking pan.

- Step 4

Bake in the preheated oven until top is golden brown, about 30 minutes.

Chicken With A Bang

Ingredients

- 1 ½ cups uncooked white rice

- 6 skinless, boneless chicken breast halves

- 2 fresh jalapeno peppers, sliced into rings

- 1 ½ cups shredded Cheddar cheese

- 12 slices bacon

- 2 tablespoons vegetable oil

- 1 teaspoon freshly ground black pepper

- ½ cup all-purpose flour

- ½ cup white wine

- 36 blue corn tortilla chips

- 1 red bell pepper, diced

- 1 cup whole kernel corn

Directions

- Step 1

In a saucepan bring 3 cups water to a boil. Add rice and stir. Reduce heat, cover and simmer for 20 minutes.

- Step 2

Using a rolling pin wrapped in plastic, pound out chicken breasts to about 1/2 inch in thickness. In the center of the breast place 2 or 3 slices of jalapeno and 3 tablespoons of cheese. Roll chicken up from the narrowest point to the widest. Wrap with 2 slices of bacon and secure with toothpicks.

- Step 3

Heat oil and black pepper in a deep skillet over medium high heat. Cook chicken wraps until they begin to brown. Reduce heat, cover and cook an additional 10 to 15 minutes, checking periodically, until chicken is no longer pink inside. Remove chicken from heat, cover and set aside.

- Step 4

Return skillet to medium high heat. To the drippings add flour, stirring to remove any lumps. Slowly add wine, stirring constantly until sauce thickens. Remove from heat.

- Step 5

In a small bowl combine red bell pepper and corn.

- Step 6

Place a medium sized mound of rice in the center of a plate. Tuck a few blue corn chips along the edge of the rice. Place chicken on rice, spoon sauce over chicken and sprinkle with 3 tablespoons of red pepper and corn mixture.

Italian Baked Cannelloni

Ingredients

- ½ cup olive oil, or as needed

- 1 pound lean ground beef

- 1 onion, thinly sliced

- ¼ teaspoon dried sage

- ¼ teaspoon dried rosemary

- salt to taste

- ½ cup white wine

- 4 tablespoons butter

- 4 tablespoons all-purpose flour

- 2 cups milk

- 2 egg yolks, lightly beaten

- 12 ounces mozzarella cheese, cubed

For the Tomato Sauce:

- 2 tablespoons butter

- 1 onion, thinly sliced

- ½ cup white wine

- 2 (14.5 ounce) cans stewed tomatoes

- salt and pepper to taste

- 12 cannelloni pasta shells

Directions

- Step 1

In a large skillet over medium heat, warm oil and saute ground beef with the onion, sage and rosemary; cook until meat is evenly browned and crumbly. Drain fat. Add salt and 1/2 cup white wine; cook until wine is evaporated. Set mixture aside.

- Step 2

To make the Bechamel sauce: Melt 4 tablespoons butter in a medium saucepan over medium heat. Add flour and stir until well incorporated. Stir in milk and bring to a slow boil until mixture thickens. Remove sauce from the heat. In a steady stream, pour the bechamel in to the beaten egg yolks, whisking constantly. Stir the sauce into the meat mixture. Stir in the cubed mozzarella.

- Step 3

In a medium saucepan over medium-low heat, melt 2 tablespoons butter and saute onion until soft and translucent. Add 1/2 cup white wine and let it cook down to evaporate; add stewed tomatoes and salt. Mix well; simmer for 15 minutes.

- Step 4

Bring a large pot of lightly salted water to a boil. Add pasta, a few at a time, and cook for 8 to 10 minutes or until al dente; using a slotted spoon, remove immediately to a pot filled with cold water. Lift pasta out with slotted spoon and arrange on a flat surface.

- Step 5

Preheat oven to 400 degrees F (200 degrees C). Lightly grease a 9x13-inch baking dish.

- Step 6

Spoon a line of filling into each shell, starting from one end and using your finger to push the filling inside of each shell. Place cannelloni in prepared baking dish and cover with tomato sauce mixture.

- Step 7

Bake in preheated oven for 15 minutes or until heated through; when finished baking, allow to stand for 5 minutes and serve.

Chorizo

Ingredients

- 3 tablespoons ground New Mexico chile

- 2 tablespoons red wine vinegar

- 1 tablespoon dried Mexican oregano

- 1 tablespoon water

- 3 cloves garlic, minced

- 1 ¾ teaspoons salt

- 1 ½ teaspoons red pepper flakes

- 1 teaspoon cumin seeds, crushed

- ¾ teaspoon white sugar

- ½ teaspoon ground black pepper

- 1 pound ground pork, well chilled

Directions

- Step 1

Combine chile powder, vinegar, oregano, water, garlic, salt, red pepper flakes, cumin seeds, sugar, and pepper in a small bowl. Mix until the salt and sugar are dissolved in the liquids.

- Step 2

Break up pork in a bowl. Pour in spice mixture and knead thoroughly. Use immediately or refrigerate to let flavors meld, 8 hours to overnight.

- Step 3

Cook and stir in a nonstick skillet over medium heat until browned and crumbly, about 10 minutes.

Dairy-Free Coconut Rice Pudding

Ingredients

- 4 cups canned coconut milk, shaken

- ¼ cup cane sugar

- 1 teaspoon vanilla extract

- 1 cup long grain white rice

Directions

- Step 1

Combine coconut milk, sugar, and vanilla extract in a medium pot and stir until combined. Add rice and bring to a boil over medium heat, about 5 minutes. Cook, gently stirring, until rice has softened and mixture has a slightly soupy but not too drippy consistency, about 20 minutes.

- Step 2

Spoon into small serving dishes. Serve warm or place in refrigerator to chill.

Muddy Hearts

Ingredients

- 1 egg

- 1 cup crunchy peanut butter

- 1 cup white sugar

- 1 (12 ounce) package milk chocolate chips

Directions

- Step 1

Preheat the oven to 350 degrees F (175 degrees C).

- Step 2

Line a baking sheet with parchment paper.

- Step 3

Combine egg, peanut butter and sugar in a bowl. The dough should be slightly dry; add small amounts of sugar if it seems too wet.

- Step 4

Place dough between two sheets of wax paper and roll to 1/2 inch thickness.

- Step 5

Cut the dough with a heart-shaped cookie cutter.

- Step 6

Place the hearts on the prepared baking sheet.

- Step 7

Bake in the preheated oven until the edges are golden, 7 to 10 minutes.

- Step 8

Cool completely on the baking sheet.

- Step 9

Melt the chocolate chips in the microwave at 30 second intervals until fully melted, stirring between intervals.

- Step 10

Dip the bottom and sides of each cookie in the melted chocolate.

- Step 11

Place cookies on wax paper to dry.

Soothing Hot Ginger Tea

Ingredients

- 1 (12 fl oz) can ginger ale (such as Canada Dry®)

- 1 black tea bag (such as Lipton®)

Directions

- Step 1

Pour ginger ale into a microwave-safe mug. Heat in the microwave for 1 to 2 minutes.n

- Step 2

Steep tea bag in the hot ginger ale for 3 to 5 minutes.n

Cold Spicy Noodles (Leng Mian)

Ingredients

- 4 ounces spaghetti, or as needed

Sauce:

- 2 cups very cold ice water

- ½ cup white vinegar

- 2 tablespoons soy sauce

- 2 tablespoons white sugar

- 2 teaspoons sambal oelek (chile paste)

- ½ teaspoon salt

Garnish:

- 1 cucumber, cut into matchsticks

- ½ cup kimchi

- ¼ cup roasted peanuts

- 1 hard-cooked egg, halved (Optional)

- 2 slices deli ham, cut into bite-sized pieces (Optional)

Directions

- Step 1

Bring a large pot of lightly salted water to a boil. Cook spaghetti in the boiling water, stirring occasionally, until tender yet firm to the bite, about 12 minutes.

- Step 2

Meanwhile, combine ice water, vinegar, soy sauce, sugar, and sambal oelek in a bowl. Refrigerate sauce to chill until spaghetti is cooked.

- Step 3

Rinse cooked spaghetti in cold water until totally cooled off; drain well.

- Step 4

Divide sauce between 2 chilled servings bowls. Add equal amounts of spaghetti, cucumber, kimchi, peanuts, egg, and ham to each bowl. Serve immediately.

Broccoli and Leftover Mashed Potato Soup

Ingredients

- 2 teaspoons bacon drippings

- 1 onion, diced

- 4 stalks celery, chopped

- 1 pound bulk pork sausage

- 1 teaspoon dried sage

- ½ teaspoon paprika

- salt and ground black pepper to taste

- 4 cups finely chopped broccoli florets

- 4 cups reduced-sodium vegetable broth

- 4 cups leftover mashed potatoes

- 1 (15 ounce) can whole kernel corn, drained

- 1 (7 ounce) can diced green chilies

- 2 cups sour cream

Directions

- Step 1

Heat bacon drippings in a large, deep saucepan or soup pot over medium-high heat. Add onion and celery; saute until softened, 3 to 5 minutes. Add sausage, sage, paprika, salt, and pepper; continue to saute, mashing up the sausage into small pieces until browned and no longer pink, 5 to 7 minutes.

- Step 2

While sausage is cooking, poke several holes in a zip-top bag and add broccoli (this allows steam to escape). Microwave for 3 minutes.

- Step 3

Pour broth into sausage mixture, then add mashed potatoes. Mix well, then add the broccoli, corn, and green chilies. Stir to combine all well and then add the sour cream. Taste and add more salt and pepper as needed. Let simmer for about 10 more minutes for flavors to meld.

Cherry Ginger Infused Tea

Ingredients

- 1 cup pitted cherries

- 1 (2 inch) piece fresh ginger, peeled and sliced

- 3 tablespoons white sugar

- 4 cups filtered water, divided

- 4 (2 g) bags green tea

- 4 lemon slices

- 1 tablespoon lemon juice, or to taste

Directions

- Step 1

Combine cherries and ginger slices in a glass bowl. Sprinkle sugar over the cherries mixture and cover with 2 cups filtered water.n

- Step 2

Cover bowl with plastic wrap and refrigerate 2 hours to overnight.n

- Step 3

Bring 2 cups filtered water nearly to a boil; pour over tea bags in a pitcher. Steep tea for 90 seconds. Squeeze tea bags into pitcher and discard bags.n

- Step 4

Strain cherry-ginger water into pitcher with green tea, squeezing out excess liquid. Serve with lemon slices and lemon juice.n

Avocado Shrimp Ceviche-Estillo Sarita

Ingredients

- 2 pounds large shrimp - peeled, deveined and chopped

- ¾ cup fresh lime juice

- 5 roma (plum) tomatoes, diced

- 1 white onion, chopped

- ½ cup chopped fresh cilantro

- 1 tablespoon Worcestershire sauce

- 1 tablespoon ketchup

- 1 teaspoon hot pepper sauce

- salt and pepper to taste

- 1 avocado - peeled, pitted and diced

- 16 saltine crackers

Directions

- Step 1

Place the shrimp and lime juice into a large bowl, and stir to coat. Let stand for about 5 minutes, or until shrimp are opaque. The lime juice will cook them. Mix in the tomatoes, onion, and cilantro until coated with lime juice; cover and refrigerate for 1 hour.

- Step 2

Remove from the refrigerator, and mix in the Worcestershire sauce, ketchup, hot sauce, salt and pepper. We have our own hot sauce recipe, but you can use whatever hot sauce you like, or leave it out and let people add their own when serving.

- Step 3

Serve in glass tumblers and top with avocado pieces. Set out extra Worcestershire sauce, ketchup, lime wedges and hot sauce for people to individualize their dish. Serve with saltine crackers.

Pick-Me-Up Egg Drop Soup

Ingredients

- 1 (16 ounce) can chicken broth

- ½ teaspoon soy sauce

- ½ teaspoon sesame oil, or to taste

- ¼ cup finely broken udon noodles

- 2 teaspoons water

- 1 teaspoon cornstarch (Optional)

- 2 eggs, beaten

- sea salt to taste

- freshly ground black pepper to taste

Directions

- Step 1

Combine chicken broth, soy sauce, and sesame oil together in a small saucepan; bring to a boil. Stir udon pieces into broth and cook, stirring occasionally, until cooked through but are still firm to the bite, 10 to 12 minutes.

- Step 2

Whisk water and cornstarch together in a bowl. Whisk cornstarch mixture into broth mixture until smooth and thickened slightly. Gradually pour in eggs, stirring gently and constantly, until eggs are wispy and cooked through, 2 to 3 minutes. Season with sea salt and black pepper.

Iced Coffee Perfection

Ingredients

- 6 cups cold water

- 1 cup ground coffee beans

- 1 tablespoon vanilla extract

- 1 tablespoon ground cinnamon

Directions

- Step 1

Mix water, coffee, vanilla extract, and cinnamon together in a jar or resealable container. Stir well. Let coffee stand (no refrigeration necessary) until flavors intensify, 8 hours to overnight.n

- Step 2

Strain coffee through cheesecloth into a separate container.

Pineapple Upside Down Cake from DOLE

Ingredients

- 1 (20 ounce) can DOLE® Pineapple Slices

- 2 tablespoons margarine, melted

- ¼ cup packed brown sugar

- 8 cherries maraschino cherries

- 1 (9 ounce) package yellow cake mix

Directions

- Step 1

Spray pan with non-stick cooking spray. Drain pineapple.

- Step 2

Stir together melted margarine and brown sugar in 8-inch cake pan. Place pineapple slices in sugar mixture. Place cherry in center of each pineapple slice and in the center of the pan.

- Step 3

Prepare cake mix according to the package directions. Pour cake batter evenly over pineapple.

- Step 4

Bake at 350 degrees F, 25 to 30 minutes or until toothpick inserted in center comes out clean.

- Step 5

Cool 5 minutes. Loosen edges and turn out onto serving platter.

South of the Border Shrimp and Grits

Ingredients

- 1 (12 fluid ounce) can evaporated milk

- ½ cup yellow grits

- ½ cup chicken broth

- 1 tablespoon salted butter

- ⅓ cup grated sharp Cheddar cheese

- 3 slices bacon

- ¾ cup frozen bell peppers

- ⅓ pound frozen medium shrimp - thawed, shelled, and deveined

- ½ teaspoon taco seasoning mix

- 2 teaspoons hot sauce, or to taste (Optional)

Directions

- Step 1

Combine evaporated milk, grits, chicken broth, and butter in a saucepan over medium-high heat; bring to a boil. Cook, stirring constantly, until thickened, 5 to 7 minutes. Add Cheddar cheese and stir until incorporated. Remove from the heat and set aside.

- Step 2

Place bacon in a large skillet and cook over medium-high heat, turning occasionally, until crisp and browned, about 3 minutes per side. Drain bacon slices on paper towels and chop when cool enough to handle.

- Step 3

Add bell peppers to the bacon grease. Add shrimp and taco seasoning. Cook and stir until peppers are heated through and shrimp are bright pink on the outside and the meat is opaque, 3 to 5 minutes. Stir in chopped bacon.

- Step 4

Place a dollop of grits in each bowl and top with shrimp mixture and hot sauce.

Chelsea Buns

Ingredients

- 2 (.25 ounce) envelopes active dry yeast

- 1 teaspoon white sugar

- ¼ cup warm water

- 6 cups all-purpose flour

- 1 teaspoon salt

- ¾ cup butter

- 1 ½ cups milk

- ¾ cup white sugar, divided

- 3 eggs, beaten

- ¼ cup butter, melted

- 1 cup raisins

- 1 egg yolk

- 2 tablespoons water

Directions

- Step 1

Sprinkle the yeast over 1/4 cup of warm water in a small bowl and stir in 1 teaspoon of sugar. The water should be no more than 100 degrees F (40 degrees C). Let stand for 5 minutes until the yeast softens and begins to form a creamy foam.

- Step 2

Sift together the flour and salt. Cut in 3/4 cup butter with a knife or pastry blender until the mixture resembles coarse crumbs. Bring the milk to a boil; remove from the heat and stir in

1/2 cup sugar. Cool until the milk is lukewarm, no more than 100 degrees F (40 degrees C). Pour the milk and yeast mixture into the flour. Add the eggs and mix well to form a soft, sticky dough.

- Step 3

Turn the dough out onto a well-floured surface and knead until smooth and elastic, about 8 minutes. Add more flour a tablespoon at a time, if necessary. Place the dough in a buttered bowl, turning to coat the dough. Cover with a light cloth and let rise in a warm place (80 to 95 degrees F (27 to 35 degrees C)) until doubled in volume, about 1 1/2 hours.

- Step 4

Roll the dough into a square on a floured surface. Brush the dough with the melted butter and sprinkle with the remaining 1/4 cup sugar and the raisins. Roll up the dough to form a log, pinching the seam to seal.

- Step 5

Preheat an oven to 375 degrees F (190 degrees C). Grease a 9x13-inch baking pan.

- Step 6

Cut the log into slices about 1 1/2 inches thick. Place the slices in the prepared pan and let them rise for 30 minutes. Beat the egg yolk with 2 tablespoons of water to form an egg wash. Brush the buns with egg wash.

- Step 7

Bake in the preheated oven until the buns are golden brown and the centers are set, about 25 minutes.

Impossibly Easy Chicken Pot Pie

Ingredients

- 1 ⅓ cups Green Giant™ Steamers™ frozen mixed vegetables

- 1 cup cut-up cooked chicken

- 1 (10.75 ounce) can condensed cream of chicken soup

- 1 cup Original Bisquick® mix

- ½ cup milk

- 1 egg

Directions

- Step 1

Heat oven to 400 degrees F. Mix vegetables, chicken and soup in ungreased glass pie plate, 9x1-1/4 inches.

- Step 2

Stir together remaining ingredients with fork until blended. Pour into pie plate.

- Step 3

Bake 30 minutes or until golden brown.

Hamburger Stew with Potatoes

Ingredients

- 1 pound ground beef

- 3 cups water

- 2 (8 ounce) cans tomato sauce

- 4 medium potatoes, peeled and chopped

- 2 medium tomatoes, chopped, or more to taste

- ¼ cup chopped white onion

- 1 (1.41 ounce) package sazon seasoning (such as Goya®)

- 2 cubes beef bouillon

- 1 clove garlic, minced, or more to taste

- ½ teaspoon chili powder

- ½ teaspoon ground cayenne pepper, or to taste (Optional)

- 1 large bay leaf

- ground black pepper to taste

- 4 ounces frozen mixed vegetables (such as Birds Eye®)

Directions

- Step 1

Heat a large nonstick skillet over medium-high heat. Cook and stir ground beef in the hot skillet until browned and crumbly, 5 to 7 minutes. Drain and discard grease.

- Step 2

Transfer beef to a large pot and add water, tomato sauce, potatoes, tomatoes, onion, sazon, bouillon cubes, garlic, chili powder, cayenne pepper, bay leaf, and black pepper. Bring to a boil over medium-high heat. Reduce heat to medium-low and simmer for 10 minutes. Add frozen vegetables and continue to cook until potatoes are tender, about 10 minutes more.

Amy's Amazing Baked Chicken Breasts

Ingredients

- 2 skin-on, boneless chicken breasts

- 4 ounces horseradish-chive compound butter

- 1 yellow onion, cut into 5 whole slices

- 2 cups chicken stock

- salt and freshly ground black pepper to taste

Directions

- Step 1

Preheat the oven to 350 degrees F (175 degrees C).

- Step 2

Using 2 fingers, loosen the skin on each chicken breast. Thinly slice compound butter and stuff under skin to cover as much of the chicken as possible.

- Step 3

Layer onion slices on the bottom of a glass baking dish. Pour in chicken stock. Place chicken breasts on top of the onions, skin-side up. Season with salt and pepper.

- Step 4

Bake in the preheated oven for 30 minutes. Start basting chicken with its juices and rotate if skin is not crisping evenly. Continue baking until chicken is no longer pink in the center and the juices run clear, about 25 more minutes, depending on the size of the chicken breasts. Baste chicken every 5 to 10 minutes. An instant-read thermometer inserted into the center should read at least 165 degrees F (74 degrees C).

CONCLUSION

It can take some time, teamwork, and determination to find the right treatment for your ulcers, but keep in mind that ulcers can be cured.

In addition to a treatment plan agreed upon by you and your doctor, you can incorporate natural approaches with healthful foods that may give you some relief and accelerate healing.

Adding plenty of fresh fruits and vegetables to your diet and reducing alcohol intake will almost certainly get you on the road to health.

Made in the USA
Monee, IL
16 July 2023